GW00865779

Look at the Picture

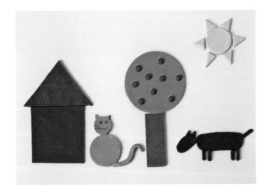

by Anne Giulieri

photography by Sylvia Kreinberg

Look at the square.

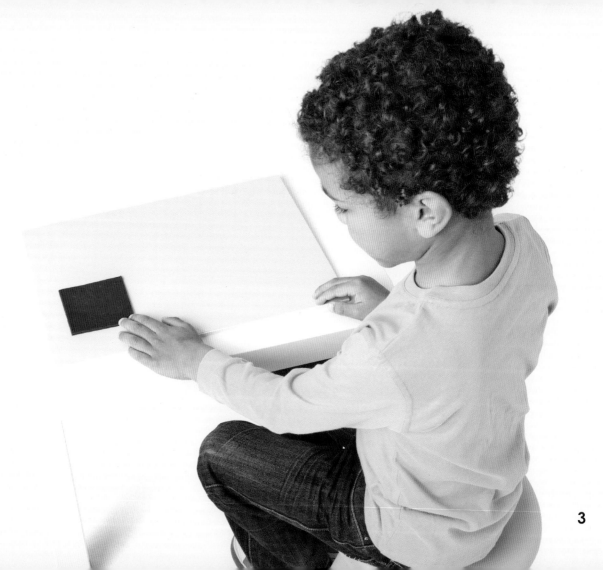

Look at the triangle.

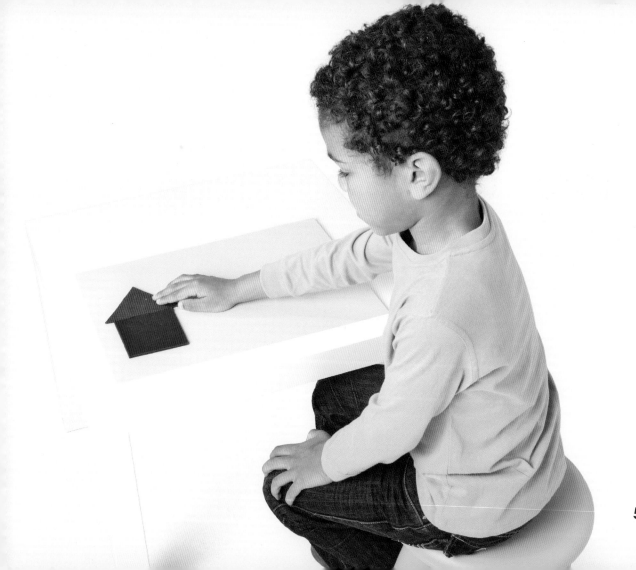

5

Look at the house.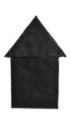

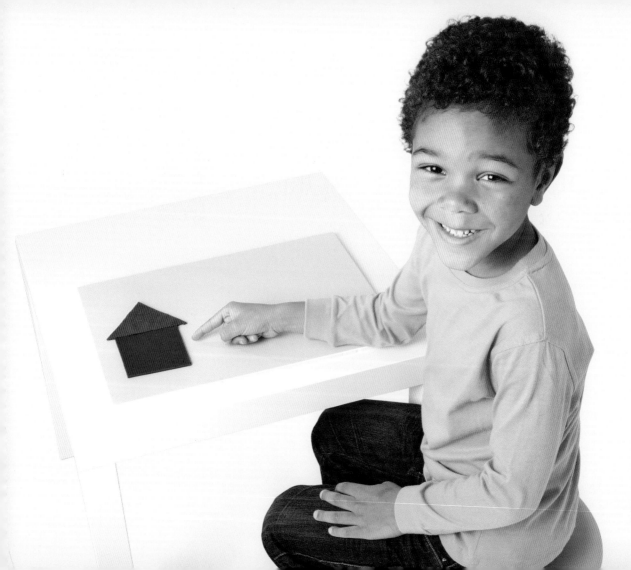

Look at the sun.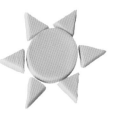

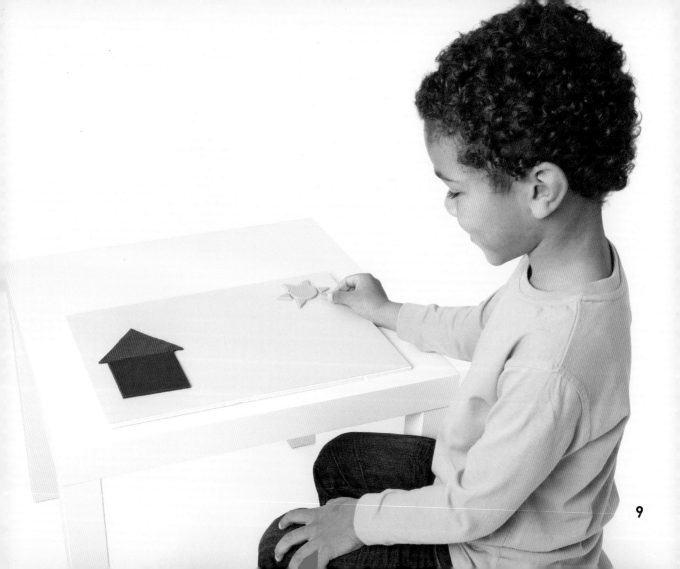

Look at the tree.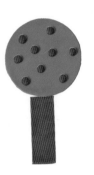

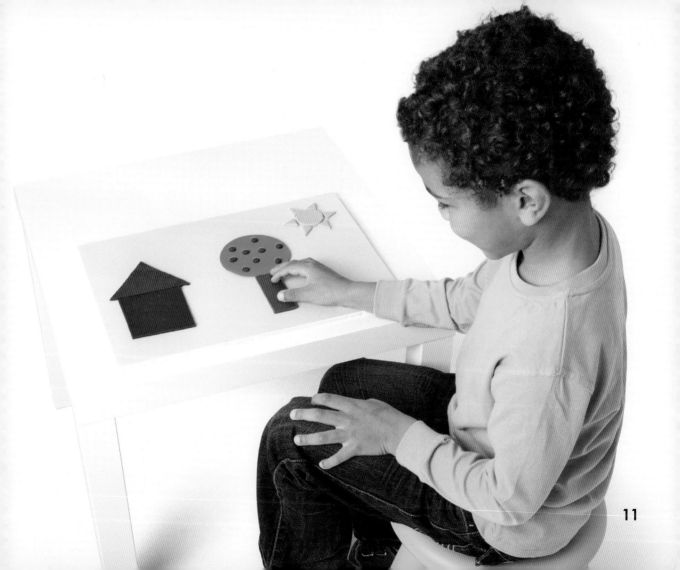

Look at the cat.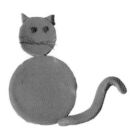

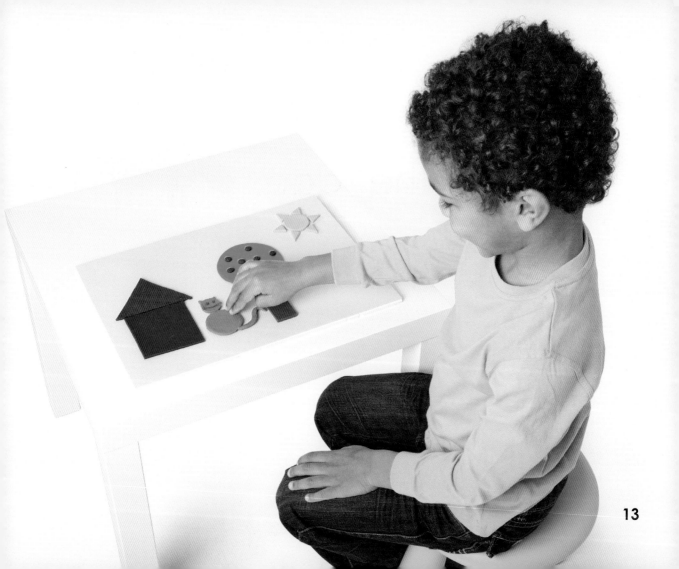

Look at the dog.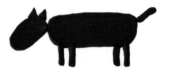

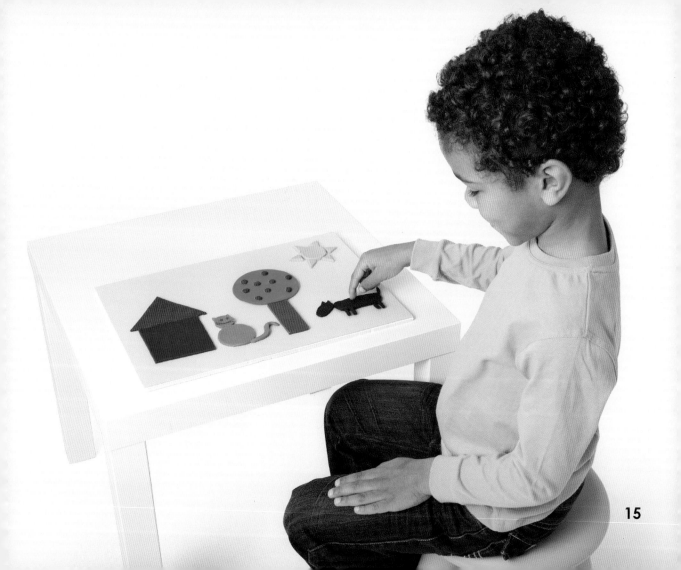

Look at the picture.

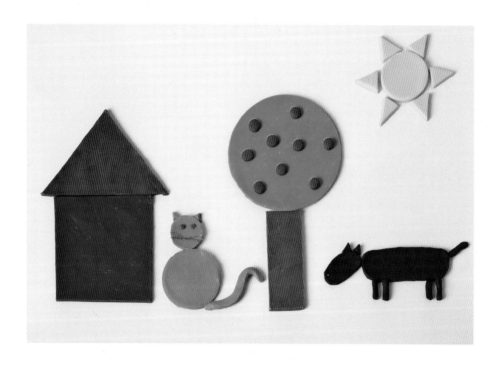